Contents

CHAPTER ONE

Going on a Summer Holiday

Summer was approaching – and, with it, the pleasant prospect of a holiday. Anne, George, Dick and Julian found themselves discussing the matter one evening. They were in an excellent mood, having just finished second helpings of Anne's wonderful moussaka, and conversation passed on to Greek food, and holidays in Greece, and so on.

'Hey – I've just thought of a game,' said Julian. 'Places that sound like they should be in other places.'

George and Anne looked at him with all the animation of statues.

'I'll go first,' Julian said. 'Tripoli. Should be in Italy, is in Libya.'

'Oh, I see,' said Anne. 'Me next.' She thought for a moment, then said victoriously, 'Lahore! Should be in France,' she said, 'is in Pakistan.'

'Okay,' said George. 'My turn. Dunkirk. Should be in Scotland, is in France.'

Julian nodded, impressed, and Anne clapped.

Whenever talking about holidays, the group always had the same conversation, Dick realized, as he listened. First they talked about the one time they had all gone together to the south of Spain. The same several anecdotes were worked through, starting with the time Julian had given a cab driver the wrong address, inadvertently saying an extremely rude word. Then they mentioned the time they'd been out in a nightclub and George had thought some moody guy was ogling her, and tried to lamp him, only to find she'd punched a mirror.

Dick nodded along, smiling politely. He knew that now they would talk about all their childhood holidays in Dorset, and how magical they had been – if also rather dangerous. 'But that just added to the fun,' he knew Anne would say, in stark contradiction of the terror he had watched her experience at the time.

Then the conversation would turn to the possibility of going back to Dorset for a holiday this summer. Everyone would demur, citing the fact that they had been there so many times before, and saying there were so many other places to go.

And then the same people would instantly recant their demurrals, and say that it was always so nice to see Fanny and Quentin, and to visit their old haunts. Then, soon as you

*George and Anne looked at him with all
the animation of statues.*

like, they'd all be planning to go on holiday to the same few square miles they'd always visited. Beautiful as the place might be, Dick felt he had seen too much of it. There were so many other options available, and they were all calling to him.

Dick saw this whole conversation in advance. And, with somewhat monotonous inevitability, it unfolded exactly as he had predicted.

'What do you think, Dick?' asked Anne.

This was a mere nicety. Dick didn't disagree with things. George disagreed with things, and Julian objected to her disagreements. But Dick himself never offered any objections to the overall plan.

Dick realized that this was his role in life – at least in the eyes of the others – at the same moment that he was asked for his consent. 'No,' he said. 'No, I don't think I'm that bothered, actually.'

He looked away, to indicate how casual this remark was supposed to be. In fact, he feared it would be like a social hand grenade going off in the group. No one had ever rejected the others and decided to go off on their own before. It could be the start of the end for them.

Ideally, there would have been a window nearby, through which he could examine the weather. But there was none.

Instead, he ended up looking into Timmy's basket. Seeing what Timmy was up to, he looked at the ceiling.

'Dick?' Anne repeated. 'Don't you want to go on holiday with us?'

'What? Oh, yeah, sure,' Dick said, turning back to them with an unconvincing semblance of surprise. 'It's always fun. I just thought I might do something by myself this summer.'

Dick noticed how nervous he was about the reception of this statement.

But the others just nodded.

'Good idea,' Julian said. 'We spend much too much time in each other's pockets, anyway.'

George was relieved that it had been Dick who had said it, as she'd long been thinking the same thing. She was surprised that someone else had spoken up first.

For Anne, it made quite a pleasant change to be thrown back on her own devices, and she relished doing something a bit different this year. She had so many friends who were always saying they wished she'd come on a trip with them. She'd pick one.

They all agreed it was a splendid idea, and started to make plans.

CHAPTER TWO

Dick Books a Holiday

When he mentioned it to several of his friends, Dick was flattered to find that they were very enthusiastic about going on holiday with him. He was surprised that they were planning on going to Marbella, when he thought there were probably much nicer places, with more to see, more to do, and fewer English people in them.

'Stop thinking like Julian,' he told himself. 'And just go with it. It's your mates you want to see, after all.'

He joined them for a pint after work one evening to discuss the holiday.

'So, why Marbella?' he asked tentatively. 'I mean, what will we do there?'

'Drink lager,' said one of them. The others cheered.

'Yes, but . . .' Dick said. 'That's not all. Is it?'

'The football will be on,' said another. This provoked another cheer.

'We could watch the football anywhere,' Dick politely

*He knew that now they would talk about all their
childhood holidays in Dorset, and how magical they
had been – if also rather dangerous.*

observed, his eyes turning to the screen above their heads, which was showing a match now.

'Yeah,' said a third mate. 'But it's Marbella!'

The lads cheered for a third time. But Dick failed to find this an entirely convincing argument. He reminded himself once more that it was the company rather than the destination that he was interested in, and he agreed to go along with them.

Almost immediately, he found he had also agreed to book the hotel for them – the others complaining of a variety of cash-flow problems that prevented them from doing it themselves. They were terribly grateful.

That evening, he tried to book the hotel, and discovered that for some reason he found it almost impossible to do. Owing to the fact that he spent so much time with his brother, sister and cousin, it seemed as though he had hardly ever booked anything before.

What's more, he was one of those people who resist being tied down to details, and who find discussion of money tedious. When forced to concentrate on it, he felt at sea, and as though he'd rather think about almost anything else. After his first four attempts to sit down and get on with it, for instance, he found that his room was suddenly tidy, his washing had been done, his household chores completed ahead of deadline and his football boots cleaned.

Every time he went to sit at the computer, a numb, woozy feeling descended over him and his brain switched off. He found himself checking and rechecking the handful of websites he usually looked at during lunchtime at work, and growing resentful that no dramatic news stories had emerged in the few minutes since he had last checked.

He noticed what he was doing, and forced himself to go back again and book the holiday this time. The second he was at the hotel website, he felt sluggish again. The site instructed him to open up an account. He was requested to insert and reinsert a password, which he was then informed, rather sternly, was unusable.

He was put out. 'Every *other* website allows me to use "bumbrainjulian",' he muttered. He simply added two numbers to the end, and wrote it down on a napkin. Once the account was active and approved, he was invited to enter his new password to log in, which seemed to him impressively pointless, as he had entered it twice not ten seconds earlier. This was all accompanied by a fog of self-doubt. He felt rather as though he was taking an examination in a second language.

Next, Dick was asked to enter his preferred dates. This didn't seem to work the first five times, and then, the sixth time, for no apparent reason, it allowed him on to the next screen.

'So, why Marbella?' Dick asked tentatively.
'I mean, what will we do there?'

YOU ARE NOT ALLOWED TO ENTER DATES THAT ARE IN THE PAST, was the message in front of him. Dick stared at it, baffled, before realizing that he had been trying to book a July holiday slap bang in the middle of the First World War. He corrected the dates, and checked the prices.

His pulse quickened – there was an 'early bird' special offer. If he paid up front, he could get twenty-five per cent off for everyone. He would be a hero. He checked the dates again, all excitement. It all seemed to fit. He was nailing this!

He went through to the payment screen, entered his debit-card details, and was then forwarded to his bank's screen for verification. He was asked for the third, sixth and tenth digits of his online-banking security password. He didn't know what this was.

He began to feel the holiday slipping from his grasp. He phoned his bank and, after getting on the line with a helpful young woman, he was asked for his telephone-banking code. He did not know this either. He was about to beg for clemency and ask if there was any other way to establish his identity, when the battery on his phone died.

He looked at the blank handset, and realized for the first time why people used to have landlines. By now, the transaction had timed out on the screen, and he was thrown back to the first page, where he was asked to enter his preferred dates again. He went to bed, fed up.

After breakfast the next Saturday morning, Dick was stretching and contemplating a day of perfect freedom when a stray thought reminded him that, by definition, an 'early bird' offer wasn't going to last forever.

'Get it over with, once and for all,' he muttered, opening his laptop, 'and then enjoy your Saturday.' He looked out of the living-room window, at the people strolling up and down the high street: browsing and chatting, holding hands.

The second he turned his attention to the computer screen, he was assailed by the familiar drowsy torpor. On a bright spring Saturday, when he should be outside, it seemed to hit him harder than on a weeknight.

He tried to find the same hotel as before, and wracked his brains for the search terms he'd used. Soon enough, he was browsing for other holiday destinations and wondering if he could persuade the guys away from Marbella. He even looked at some in Dorset, out of sheer habit, and noticed there happened to be a hotel there with the same name – La Credenza.

He got out his debit card, ready.

*

Dick came to.

He stared about him, saw it was two p.m. He was aghast
– *where* had three hours gone? He feared for a moment that
he was suffering from some sort of aphasia or stroke, but
then recalled he had spent an hour looking at the *Daily Mail*
wall of shame, then another hour reading the tedious things
his acquaintances were saying on Facebook. Then his mind
had wandered – open on the screen in front of him was the
Wikipedia page for Ernest Borgnine.

'Come on, Dick,' he told himself. 'This is pathetic. *Concentrate* . . .'

The hotel was called La Credenza – he remembered that.
He quickly found the website again, but it seemed to have
undergone some sort of renovation in the few days since
he had last been on it. The prices had changed, as had the
photos of the rooms.

But Dick adamantly *refused* to be fazed. He found what he
thought were roughly the same rooms as before – in fact, the
best deal was on one double twin, which could take all four
of them. He'd been on lads' holidays in the past, with Julian,
and he knew that no one cared about sharing – especially if
it saved them a few quid.

He went to pay, and was once again confronted by the
obstacle of his online-banking security code. He phoned up

the bank to have it reset, and in doing so, of course, had to request a new telephone-banking security number.

'We'll send it to you by email,' this new, equally helpful young woman said.

Dick sat at his computer for fifteen minutes, refreshing the email account, and then rang them again.

'No problem,' said this, third, no less pleasant and helpful woman. 'I'll have to send you another new code, if the other didn't come through.'

'But that's not the issue; I was wondering if perhaps you don't have my correct email address?'

'I'm afraid I can't tell you the one we have, as you haven't confirmed your identity to me. To do that, you need to have your telephone-banking security number.'

For the first time since he was ten years old, Dick started to feel he might cry.

'Just log into your online banking to see copies of any email we've sent you.'

'But I don't have my online code; that's what I was phoning to try and change.'

'That's your *verification* code, for online purchases,' said the pleasant woman. 'To get access to your account, you just need to use the device we sent you. It looks like a little calculator.'

At long last, Dick felt he might have seen a glimmer of light at the end of the tunnel. He thanked the woman and rang off. He went to the kitchen drawer in which all such things were kept, and then to his own desk. Then he checked the pockets in his coats, and all through his record bag, rucksack and the three last wallets he had owned, which for reasons unclear were kept in a heap on the mantelpiece.

By now, he was getting a deep headache from the combination of depression and panic he was feeling. He rubbed his temples and thought he'd sit down for a second.

'Have you been here all day?' asked George, heaving her backpack on to the sofa. She had just jogged back from rock-climbing. She shone with sweat and the smugness of one who has just been exercising.

Dick looked round at her from the armchair. He saw it was ten to eight.

'Oh, *shit*!' he said.

A sit-down and a cup of tea had, without any particular intention, turned into a six-hour session of *Horizon: Zero Dawn* on the PS4.

Getting up and going to his room, Dick now attacked his task with something approaching berserk fury. He phoned the bank again, dimly aware that the lines might close at eight p.m. He abandoned his usual diffidence for a very uncharacteristic forthrightness. He explained it was a big emergency and that he *must* have access to his bank account. He demanded that he be allowed to answer any number of personal questions in order to establish his identity, and just stopped short of saying that it was a matter of life and death.

This done, he set up a new telephone-banking security number and a new online verification code. He wrote them in large letters and taped them to the wall, in direct contra-vention of the bank's instructions.

Then he hacked away at his laptop: implacably filling and re-filling every form; ticking or unticking every necessary box; fulfilling every request, no matter how demented or repe-titious. At last he received an email confirming his booking.

He leant back in his chair with his hands behind his head, and spotted the napkin on which he had written the account details for the hotel's website. He frowned – why hadn't he been asked to enter those? Then he saw the subject line of the email.

Congratulations! it read. *You are going to Dorset!*

He immediately saw where the confusion had arisen. There was a hotel called La Credenza in Marbella, which offered an early-bird deal. But, there was one on the Dorset coast that did too ...

*Dick's pulse quickened – there was
an 'early bird' special offer.*

There were some acts of stupidity to which Dick just could not bear to confess. And so it was with a heavy heart that he opened an email to the boys.

Hey, guys, it said, *I'm sorry to say that, owing to circumstances beyond my control, I won't be able to join you in Marbella this summer . . .*

Now all he had to do was completely reverse his previous position and try to convince Julian, George, Anne and Timmy to come with him to Dorset, after all . . .

CHAPTER THREE

Waxing Critical

Dick found it surprisingly easy to persuade the others to join him. It turned out that, left to their own devices for the first time in years – ever, really – their minds had all gone blank. It seemed they didn't really have friends who were the going-on-holiday-with kind. So, no one had got around to organizing anything, and when Dick said he'd got a good deal for a hotel on the south coast, they all agreed readily. Dick wrote it on the calendar.

'So,' said Julian, looking over Dick's shoulder as he wrote. 'Two months until we go. Better get beach body ready!'

This elicited a snort from George, a groan from Dick and a cold silence from Anne, as she stuffed clothes into the washer.

This talk of the 'beach body' was a private joke between the housemates. For, the previous summer, they had gone on a beach holiday and had really made the effort to look good. It had been a disaster.

It had started when George found an article on the kitchen table entitled 'Lose Seven Pounds in Seven Days!'

'*Come on, Dick,*' *he told himself.*
'*This is pathetic. Concentrate . . .*'

'That's a good idea, actually,' she'd said to Julian, when he came in a moment later. 'You'll feel a lot better.'

'It's nothing to do with me,' he said with disgust. 'It must be Anne's.'

This proved, indeed, to be the case. 'If you lose seven pounds, you'll be invisible,' George told her, when Anne got in. But Anne was not impressed.

'I'll thank you to mind your own business,' she said. She was feeling rather fed up, and was not interested in being lectured. She had spent the afternoon shopping for suitable beach accoutrements – something she had expected would be fun. It was not.

Until that day, Anne had gloried in the possession of an entirely bulletproof self-esteem, when it came to her physicality. This was because even at her worst she looked like a young Grace Kelly who'd put the effort in and really scrubbed up a treat. Today, that had changed.

There was just *something about* the mirrors in fitting rooms. They hated her. Had it always been this way?

Having visited three successive changing rooms in different department stores, Anne felt that each must have required an army of highly skilled technicians working around the clock for weeks in order to achieve such a disastrously unflattering effect. Whether it was the placement, the lighting, the ambience, the very materials used to make the mirrors themselves, the pappy muzak or the drab fittings and fixtures, she couldn't tell. But she had suddenly discovered great tracts of herself she hadn't known were there. So much skin. And the skin's texture: like used teabags. And the *colour*: glazier's putty.

She was decidedly unhappy about the whole business, and therefore gave George short shrift when it came to reading articles about weight loss.

Before long, she was not the only one in the house who was facing up to body issues.

Walking in on Anne waxing her legs in the bathroom later that night, Julian made the usual predictable remarks – 'How can you do that to yourself?' and so on – but once more, Anne was not impressed. In fact, she pointed out that he was in dire need of trying it himself.

'I've never heard such rubbish,' he said. 'There's nothing so manly as a hairy chest. I like it. The chicks dig it.'

'Whether these so-called "chicks" dig or do not dig it, and I can't imagine what chi— *women* you might be talking about,' Anne said coldly, 'it is not your chest that concerns me. Nor your arms; you can put those away, as well. No. Look at your hands.'

'These things?' he said, holding them up. He had never

really thought about it before, but there was something of the mid-transformation werewolf about them. 'I suppose you could say they're a tad hirsute,' he conceded.

'They're *appalling*,' Anne said. 'Here.' And before he'd really had a chance to think about what she was doing, she'd pasted the back of both of his hands with wax.

'Great,' she said. 'Now, smooth this over it, and then pull it off very quickly.' And she handed him a little strip of fabric.

'Ha,' said Julian.

'I'm not joking, Julian.'

'You'd better be,' he said. 'Because I'm not pulling *any-thing* off. So to speak.'

Anne shrugged, and attended once more to her own legs. She hummed quietly to herself.

Julian's smile, which had been fading, now vanished utterly. He looked at the fast-stiffening beige paste on the back of his hands, and then at the same stuff on Anne's legs. He opened his mouth, emitted a sound rather like the yelp of a small animal being strangled, and looked at Anne again.

'You've really done this?' he asked, when the power of speech had returned to him. He held his hands up in front of him, as though they were hands no longer, but exhibits in a court of law.

Anne sighed. 'It's really not a big deal. Why do you have to make such a song and dance about everything?'

'How dare you entrap me into taking part in your cultish gender rituals! How am I supposed to pull this stuff off?'

'Easy. Like this,' said Anne. And, scrunching her eyes shut, she gripped the fabric strip she'd been smoothing over the wax on her leg, and tore it off. It made a sickening sound, like that of cloth tearing.

Julian let out a high-pitched scream and ran from the room.

'You'll have to do it sooner or later,' said Anne through his bedroom door, fifteen minutes later.

'I don't have to do anything!' he shouted back. 'You can't make me!'

Julian held out for four days.

At first, he was confident. Having what felt like a layer of cold plastic on the back of his hand was far from convenient, of course, and it caught on things all the time, but he felt sure he could get used to this. The fact that it didn't wash off, and made showering rather unpleasant, he could stand. He assumed the wax would gradually loosen over a period of time, like a plaster, until one day it simply wouldn't be there anymore.

It was unsightly, of course, but Julian quickly got used to it and assumed others would too.

*At long last, Dick felt he might have seen a glimmer
of light at the end of the tunnel.*

This was a miscalculation. The strange looks from people on the Tube he could live with. His colleagues' queries he batted away rather ill-temperedly. But when his line manager interrupted a big meeting at work to ask with deep concern if he'd been burnt, and whether he was okay, Julian knew that this had to be dealt with.

It was done that evening, after much alcohol and many failures of nerve. George refused to do it because she could see how agonizingly squeamish it made Dick – so she insisted he had to do it. She also wanted to get as much enjoyment from it as possible, from the position of observer. Julian was incapable of performing the operation himself, and until he was two bottles of wine to the good, he would squeak when anyone came near his hands, and hide them under the table.

'Do it slowly, do it slowly,' Julian said. 'Then it won't hurt so much.'

'If you do it slowly, it will hurt *much* more,' said Anne, sighing. She was trying to do some work on her laptop and all this fuss was getting on her nerves. Acting once again before Julian had a chance to see what she was doing, she reached over, grabbed the corner of both wax patches between finger and thumb, and ripped them off.

Julian screamed. Dick yelled.

Timmy ran to the front door and back, then all round the flat, barking like mad.

He was swiftly joined by Julian, who jumped up and ran around in circles, flapping his hands, before plunging them into the freezer. Dick's face seemed to be stuck permanently in a wince. George was wiping a tear from her eye, and sighing, feeling quite laughed out.

'Have you all finished?' asked Anne.

Gradually, calm of a sort returned, broken only by Julian repeatedly pulling his hands out of the freezer, examining the reddened patches, and thrusting them back in again.

'Thank you,' said Anne. 'What brave boys you all are.'

CHAPTER FOUR

Spray de Corps

Dick had endured problems of his own, too, the previous summer. First, he had hidden from his older brother the fact that he had been invited away for a long weekend with some mates. There were dozens of perfectly good reasons for Julian not being invited too, but Dick knew that Julian wouldn't see it that way, and would be likely to overreact. So, life being short, he lied and claimed to be going on a work-related jaunt to Yorkshire, when in fact he was going on a four-day bender to Barcelona.

The trouble started when Dick covered himself with high-factor sunblock and then fell asleep on the beach after a big night out. The trouble deepened – along with his tan – when he did the same thing the next day. By the time he was catching his flight home, Dick had a deeply bronzed aspect for which the native Yorkshireman is not well known.

It was one of the guys who suggested the solution to him. 'Get a tan,' he said.

As so often with his mates' suggestions, Dick found this

'So,' said Julian, looking over Dick's shoulder
as he wrote. 'Two months until we go. Better get
beach body ready!'

less than perfectly helpful. 'I've got a tan,' he said. 'That's the problem.'

'Yeah, so get another one,' said his interlocutor. 'A lighter one. A *spray* tan,' he said.

Dick was somewhat trepidatious as he entered the tanning salon, which – perhaps because it was situated in a deconsecrated chapel on the high street – was called Let Us Spray. He felt foolish, and an imposter, bound to be found out at any second. His diffidence seemed to infect the lady in the white coat who administered the tan. She seemed to be wary of him, and not concentrating fully on her task.

'You're already beautifully tanned,' she said. 'It seems such a waste.'

'It's for the best, believe me,' said Dick. 'I promise.'

'And you definitely want the *lightest* tan?' she asked again.

Dick nodded and rigorously followed all her instructions. He was pretty sure the machine hadn't been reset after being used for someone much shorter than he, but couldn't pluck up the courage to say so.

As the tan went on, he was suspicious that he couldn't feel anything going on the top half of his face, but when he came out afterwards, the woman didn't seem to notice.

It was only when he got home that he discovered, as he had suspected, that the tan stopped at about the eyebrows. What's more, he now understood what the woman in the salon had meant. She was not saying it was a waste of her time, or the salon's precious supplies, but that the whole operation was misbegotten. Spraying a *lighter* tan on already dark skin did not lighten it. In fact, all Dick was left with was a distinct line of demarcation that ran just above his eyebrows, even though the skin either side of the line was not of a noticeably different shade.

He was somehow worse off than he had been before – no amount of explaining could make *this* believable, after all. So he miserably came clean to Julian at the first opportunity, and withstood the other's haughty silence for a whole month. During which time he also had to experience the shame of wearing a bandana.

So, the previous summer, the house's preparations for their holiday had not been entirely harmonious. Anne's attempt to lose seven pounds in seven days proved – unlike her diet – fruitless. Perversely, it was George who succeeded where Anne had failed. Stopping in the kebab shop on the way home after a Friday night in the pub with Dick and Julian, something possessed George to opt for a chicken doner.

By four a.m. she was awake and shivering. Her stomach felt like a cement mixer running at full speed, as the first effects of virulent food poisoning took hold. By six a.m. she had relocated to the bathroom for the foreseeable future, and the following day she very nearly admitted herself into hospital.

George lost just under a stone, all told, in three days. Anne insisted on caring for her, which meant that both of them would miss their flight. The boys got as far as the front door with their bags, before realizing that it just couldn't be done, to leave the other two (three, including Timmy) behind. Their holiday was quietly abandoned.

CHAPTER FIVE

Something up with Julian

'What on *earth* are you doing?' Anne asked.

Julian was lying face-down on the living-room floor. Pressing the ground with his closed fists, he performed the first half of a press-up, lifting his body until his arms were straight. He had been intending to remain in this posture for a minute or two, and regale his housemates with one of Larkin's poems about fading youth and the passage of time. But, under the pressure of his body weight, his arms weren't the steadfast girders he had expected. They were quivering like harp strings and his face had gone pale. He maintained the pose for what might generously be described as an entire moment before collapsing on the floor with a muffled expletive. It was this behaviour that had provoked Anne's question. She now repeated it.

'I said what are you *doing*, Julian?'

'Just a spot of exercise,' he said. 'You know. Get in shape. Keep in trim. Maintain the old fizz-ee-cue.'

There was just something about the mirrors in fitting rooms. They hated her. Had it always been this way?

George paused her DVD and looked over at Julian with a frown. 'The fuck are you talking about?'

Julian, still short of breath after his half push-up, regarded them gaily. 'Beach body, mate,' he said, smiling. 'No carbs till Marbs.'

George looked at Anne. Anne looked at George. They both looked at Julian.

'I'd say you'd been drinking,' said George, 'but you're not bleary and morose.'

Julian beamed at his housemates, one after the other.

'Woof,' said Timmy, suspiciously.

'Yes, Timmy,' said George. 'Maybe he *is* on drugs. I agree.'

'You're being annoying, whoever you are,' said Anne. 'Although, I'll stop short of asking you to bring Julian back. Dick, where is this hotel we're going to exactly?'

'Um,' said Dick. 'Dorset, actually.'

Everyone laughed.

'Woof!' said Timmy, with approval. 'Woof!'

'Oh, be *quiet*, Timmy,' said George.

Timmy growled as he retreated to his basket. He liked merriment among his friends, but he objected to any disparagement of his beloved Dorset – a land, to him, of the widest fields, the bluest skies and the plumpest, tastiest rabbits in existence. The rats he encountered in the parks of London were no comparison.

'So, Dorset, after all,' said Anne, smiling. 'You changed your tune, Dick.'

'I didn't change anything. I just . . .' He was going to say, *buggered up a booking for me and some other friends*, but he smarted at the droll accusations of idiocy that would surely follow. He did not care to indulge his housemates in that particular pastime. 'There was a special offer,' he said. 'We got a third off.'

'Oh! Good for you, Dick,' said Anne. 'Well done.'

'Is there a beach?' Julian asked.

'Yes. One of the best in England, as a matter of fact. At least, that's what they said.'

'Beach body time, then,' said Julian, getting up and doing more antiquated exercises in front of them. He leant against a chair while doing leg stretches, in between flashing the others with his goofy smile.

'What *is* the matter with him?' asked George.

'Maybe he's in love,' said Dick.

'Ha!' said Julian. 'They'll be queuing up for me when they see my beach body.'

'Oh, stop *saying that*,' said George. 'It's a revolting and sinister phrase. It was devised by the patriarchy for the objectification of women and the re-enforcement of long-out-dated heteronormative gender stereotypes.'

'Yeah,' said Dick.

'Not by me,' said Julian. 'I'm talking about the objecti-fication of old Julesypoos.' He lay down on the carpet and tried to do a sit-up. He'd expected to be able to do *one*, at least. But it was a struggle even to manage that, and after getting three-quarters of the way up he subsided with much squeaking and puffing. The others affected to ignore him.

What was going on with 'old Julesypoos' was that he was feeling liberated.

A few weeks earlier, when they had briefly lost Uncle Quentin at an enormous garden centre, George had given what was, to Julian at least, a convincing and horrifying speech about the pervasiveness of sexism. Julian felt that his eyes had been opened, and he was thoroughly disgusted with himself for his former blindness. After some thought, he had realized that the single most immediate and helpful response he could make was to permanently retire from the (entirely undemocratic) position of Boy in Charge. This, in turn, had brought him to a beautiful realization: being no longer in charge wasn't going to be a challenge. It was going to be a holiday.

He saw now that automatically thinking he was right, and

therefore always taking charge of what the group did, had in fact been holding him back. Although he was burdened with a certain amount of macho pride, at least he was now aware of it, and its negative effects.

He was, he realized, probably no better or wiser than any of the others, despite the fact his brain constantly told him he was. Once he switched that part of his psyche off, or tried to – or, more usefully perhaps, once he regarded that part of himself *humorously* – he had no need to tell others what to do.

It was a glorious weight off his shoulders.

From now on, if he pleased, he could be casual and thoughtless, like Dick, or conservative and brittle, like Anne. Or sarcastic and resentful, like George. But even as he had this thought, Julian noticed and rejected its negativity. These were aspects of the *old* Julian. The one who was defensive, and afraid to admit he was wrong.

Because he didn't want to be the others. He wanted to be Julian – a new chap whom he didn't entirely know yet. So far, he had discovered that this new Julian loved the feeling of having no responsibility, and just wanted to be jolly, and silly, and nice. And make his friends laugh. He was intending to find out more about this chap.

And in the meantime, the others could jolly well enjoy taking charge of these little adventures for themselves . . .

CHAPTER SIX

Beach Body Attitudes

Julian's constant mockery of the idea of getting 'beach body ready' meant that everyone was persistently aware of the upcoming holiday.

One morning, Anne made toast for herself and Julian. On seeing the meagre scraping of butter she had spread on it, Julian reached out with his knife and took a thick supplementary scoop – one so large, in fact, it rather made Anne sick to behold. Catching her eye, he smiled.

'Got to think about the beach bod,' he said, and chuckled to himself.

A few days later, for pudding, Anne served ice cream. There was only an inch left in the bottom of the tub, so everyone looked rather disconsolately at the semi-scoop they were offered on their apple crumble. Then Julian said, 'Wait!' and dived into the bottom drawer of the freezer, retrieving a further carton of Häagen-Dazs.

'Think of the beach bod,' he said, popping the top off, and stripping the plastic seal back with a flourish. No

*Julian let out a high-pitched scream and ran
from the room.*

one quite knew what to say, but they didn't refuse the ice cream.

The others weren't used to this rather jolly and whimsical Julian. More to the point, they were not used to analysing Julian. In the past, they had always had his neuroses and foibles thrust in their faces as a necessary consequence of his bossing them around. Now he had suddenly stopped, they didn't know what to make of it. And so they looked at him anew.

Then there was this 'beach bod' joke he kept making. He clearly had every intention of putting on pounds and pounds in advance of the holiday and looking as appalling as he could on the beach. And what, as Dick rather inarticulately asked Anne, was that all about?

They were vaguely aware of a news story the previous summer, which had involved an offensive advert's use of the phrase 'beach body ready', and the furore that followed, introducing them to the term 'body shaming'. They assumed that was what Julian was joking about.

Quite contrary to his intentions, however, in the run-up to the holiday this insistent joke of Julian's rather drew the others' attention towards their physiques. After the previous year's mishaps, though, they were not particularly minded to be self-conscious.

George was not so much self-conscious as hypervigilant and ready to spring if she caught so much as a whiff of body shaming happening in any direction. It didn't make her tense. If anything, it was an outlet for her native aggression, and made her more relaxed.

Anne had also been deeply affected by the speech George had given about sexism, albeit in a subtler way. Naturally, she had suffered through the white noise of male thoughtlessness, selfishness, patronization and stupidity as every other woman. But then, she was so exquisitely pretty that the offensiveness of the male population was partially offset by the swooning deference the world offered her, simply for being herself.

Now, however, she was starting to realize that she should have been making a fuss. Considering her agreeable nature, when that fuss arrived it was likely to be rather muted. But, as she thought again about what George had said, she found she *was* increasingly ready for a fight. In the meantime, she was less disposed to wear figure-hugging dresses and skirts, or flattering clothes of any kind. She did not particularly look forward to going to the beach, and wasn't at all sure if she would pack a bikini.

Dick was not so concerned with gender politics at the moment, but was still chafing about how the others perceived him. He didn't want to be seen as safe, dependable, predictable Dick any longer.

Julian, meanwhile, watched antiques shows on telly, looked on Twitter, read Muriel Spark novels, and added an extra dollop of cream to his scones (cream first, jam on top – rather the Devon method, than the madness of Cornwall). He also noticed that he spent a lot more time smiling these days.

None of them did a stroke of exercise, or prepared in any way for the beach.

CHAPTER SEVEN

Dorset Ho!

When the taxi taking them from the railway station mounted the hill and wound down towards the little cove, everyone exclaimed at the beauty of the sandy beach that was revealed.

So beautiful was the view that, when they drew up outside a rather ugly and boxy hotel covered with scaffolding, which seemed to be where La Credenza was on the map, they refused to panic. Julian and Dick darted in from the car to ask whether this was the right hotel, and were greeted by a coldly hostile young man with sad eyes and a plurality of tattoos, who informed them that the hotel was shut. This they had already intuited from the plastic sheets covering all the furniture, the workmen walking around, the sound of sawing, and the thick layer of dust on the counter.

Still they refused to panic. Dick showed the lad his booking confirmation.

'All our bookings are being fulfilled by the Old Crown, further down the beach,' the young man said dismissively, and exited the room before they could ask any more questions.

*'How dare you entrap me into taking part in your
cultish gender rituals!'*

Dick and Julian returned to the cab and relayed these new instructions.

The second hotel, when they pulled up outside it, was the opposite of the first. It was, in fact, even more picturesque than they could have hoped. It was set back from the beach, and beneath the turf-tufted lip of an overhanging cliff. It was also, to judge by its picturesque wonkiness, which was a feature throughout, of very ancient origins.

The woman on reception had pink bouffant hair and outrageously thick glasses through which she blinked enormously. She greeted them with warmth and humour, and got them up to their room in no time.

'God, we're sharing,' said George, looking at the twin double beds. 'I didn't know that.'

'Woof,' said Timmy.

'Just look at that view . . .' said Julian.

They all stopped to admire it. True, it might be a shame not to be a few thousand miles further afield and in somewhere more exotic, but on a clear, hot summer's day, the Dorset coast was undeniably stunning.

While Timmy sniffed his way round the room and settled in his basket, the other four watched holidaymakers on the road beneath the window, ambling happily and licking ice creams. Then they saw several people leap for cover as an old man drove a vintage car along the beachfront, tooting his horn and hollering at people to get out of the way. They watched him go (weaving all over the place) with fond amusement and then drifted back to their beds and bags. It didn't seem right for a place like this to be without its eccentrics, they felt.

'Right, I'm unpacked,' said Julian, about ten seconds later.

Anne, who had only just finished unzipping the first of her suitcases, looked at him sharply, and discovered this was true. He had chosen one drawer for himself and emptied his rucksack into it with one movement.

'I'll go and see what the bar's like in this place,' Julian said, tucking his paperback under his arm. 'I'll get the drinks in too. George, Guinness; Dick, session ale; Anne, white wine spritzer. Text me if you want to change your order!'

Julian delivered the last few words at a yell through the crack of the closing door, and then hummed to himself as he skipped down the stairs.

'What is *up* with him?' asked Anne.

'Shhh,' said George. 'Don't jinx it.'

The bar was agreeably beamed and low-ceilinged, adorned with bronze beer pumps, a cheerful barmaid (bar*person*, Julian corrected himself) and many polished dark-wood tables so charmingly warped and wonky they looked like they had been assembled by drunken dwarves at about the beginning of the Bronze Age.

'Perfect,' Julian said. He availed himself of a pint of session IPA and sat down to read his book.

Julian did not just like the practice of drinking; he liked the culture and literature of it too. So it was with delight he had discovered the pre-war novels of Patrick Hamilton – dark comedies, which took place almost exclusively in pubs, and dealt with weak and fearful people ruining their lives while drinking to revolting excess.

Julian bent the book back to crease the spine (a visibly lived-in paperback being far more handsome, in his opinion, than a spanking new one), took a sip of beer, propped his legs (*not* his feet) up on the stool in front of him and let out a deep sigh of contentment.

He read for a while, chuckled a few times, and looked over his shoulder, out of the window, to take in the blissful view once more. Then he settled back in his seat, reassured that he *was* really here, and enjoying himself this much.

It was a short while later that he noticed a slight pain developing around the temples. The feeling of being on holiday suddenly felt like it was slipping away, and he wondered why this could be. Julian shifted in his seat. He wasn't physically uncomfortable. What could it be?

'Thank you,' said Anne. 'What brave boys you all are.'

'Of course, these cliffs might look very old, but in geological terms they are in fact very *young*,' someone was saying. 'About as young as rock can be, in fact.'

'Oh, Peter,' said an adoring female voice. 'You are so terribly clever. How do you know so much about so much?'

'One picks things up, here and there . . .'

Julian's dissipating contentment completely vanished. It was replaced with a sudden, all-over sensation of icy dread.

George and Anne discussed Julian's recent change of spirit as they finished unpacking and then came down into the bar. George was of the opinion that they should just enjoy it while it lasted, while Anne was afraid it was a symptom of some underlying physical or mental health condition, and was half minded to urge him to visit his GP.

Dick, walking behind them, wasn't at all sure he liked this conservatism and short-sightedness in the other two. Did they expect the boys never to change, or to grow? He kept his thoughts to himself.

The three of them (four, with Timmy) found their way into the bar, commented to each other how charming it was, and then set eyes on Julian, and the drinks he had procured for them and placed around the table. Then they saw his expression.

'What the hell's the matter with you?' George asked, sitting down next to him. Then she underwent a similar transformation. Her expression froze.

Anne and Dick stared at them. They thought at first that Julian and George had both sat in something unpleasant. But then they noticed the fixity of their expressions, staring across the room. They turned to look.

'Oh,' said Dick.

On the other side of the bar, eating lunch at a table, were seven handsome young men and women who were well known to them. They had been talking and laughing among themselves, but gradually an awareness of being regarded stole over the group and conversation quietened. Then the man at the end of the table stood up and ambled over.

'What a pleasant surprise,' said Peter, leader of the Secret Seven. Behind him, at the table, his cohorts gleamed with smugness. 'Having a little getaway, Julian?'

Julian opened his mouth to speak, but then closed it again. This was the first test of his new anti-leadership of their little troupe. He refused to take charge, and so looked to the others to speak for themselves. He also reflected that this was for the best, because he was sure to have said something childishly spiteful and self-defeating, anyway.

'Your powers of deduction are undiminished,' said George. 'How did you work it out?'

'I see you've brought all your lickspittles with you,' said Anne, feeling both horrible for being rude to someone, and rather thrilled at her own daring.

Peter seemed surprised that his appearance hadn't put them out of face.

The two groups had last met the previous year, when they had found themselves attending the same team-building workshop. There had been a competitive element to the day, in which the Secret Seven had trounced the others in every category. Despite this, the four housemates (and Timmy) had eventually won by a last-minute intervention.

Julian suddenly recalled that, by the time the results had been read out at the strategy away day, the Secret Seven had gone home, meaning they probably still thought they had won. He was eager to let them know the true result. But he realized that this, too, would be self-defeating.

'Why do you guys follow us around like this?' George asked. 'It's frankly embarrassing.'

Peter chuckled. 'We were here first, so it would seem you are following us.'

'"Here first"?' Anne asked. 'That's rather a playground mentality, don't you think?'

'We come here every year,' said Barbara, coming to stand next to Peter. 'We're here for a week. I take it we'll be going up against you in the beach body competition?'

The use of the term 'beach body', which had over the last year become more than somewhat shop-soiled among the four housemates, startled them.

'Beach body competition?' George asked. 'What is this, the nineteenth century?'

'In fact,' said Peter. 'That *is* when it started. It's been held every year since the first was judged by a middle-aged Queen Victoria. And we intend to win, like we do every year. Barbara always wins Most Beautiful Lady. Although, with Anne here, you might have some competition, Barbs.'

He obviously said this to make an impact, and to stoke rivalry between the two women for his own gratification. Barbara rose to the bait splendidly, fixing Anne with a scornful stare. Anne, however, was holding out her hand and examining the ends of her nails. She ran a finger over them, to check if they were smooth.

'You win every year, do you? So they have a category for Smug Bores, do they?' Julian asked.

'Afraid not, so you might go home empty-handed,' said Peter. 'I always go in for the Best Male Body award.'

Peter was wearing a short-sleeved shirt and, to everyone's

*Dick had a deeply bronzed aspect for which the native
Yorkshireman is not well known.*

disgust (including, surely, some of his own team members), he proceeded to roll up his sleeves, flex his arms and kiss both biceps.

In the past, Anne might have felt a reluctant tug of admiration towards Peter's confidence. Not now, though. This was the behaviour, as Julian so rightly said, of a bore.

'Come on,' she said, turning to the others. 'I've lost my thirst. Let's go for a walk.'

'Come on, Timmy,' said George.

Wordlessly agreeing, the others drifted to the door. In the ten seconds it took them to do this, Julian (who hated waste) managed to finish his own pint and half of George's Guinness. He caught up with them just as they reached the door.

'The competition's on Sunday!' Peter called after them. 'I'll see you there!'

CHAPTER EIGHT

The Not-Secret-Enough Seven

The discovery of the Secret Seven in the same hotel was a bitter blow to the group. First and foremost, it meant that the hotel was not going to be a place they particularly wanted to stay and relax in.

However, it was summer, they were on holiday, and after walking along the gorgeous beach for half an hour and throwing sticks for Timmy, they could not remain fed up.

'It means that we'll have to get out and about in the countryside, and find nice things to do,' said Anne.

'That's true,' said Dick. 'What do you make of this beach body competition?'

They all made faces.

'In this day and age,' said Anne. 'Really.'

'You might actually win, though,' said Dick. He always chipped in with a compliment or encouragement for his little sister. Although, as he said this, he realized that it was redundant. For weeks or months now, he had been subconsciously

56

noting that Anne had been changing. She was less delicate; she had more of a backbone.

'I have no intention of winning or losing,' said Anne.

'Yeah,' said George. 'Why can't they do something civilized, like a pub quiz? That's a competition I can respect.'

'Hear, hear,' said Julian.

'So what will we do with our holiday?' George asked.

'Get out into the country,' said Dick.

'Maybe a bit of bathing,' said Anne.

'Possibly sample some of the local ale?' Julian asked. He was pointing up ahead of them to the top of the beach. There was another heavy-timbered building, almost as old as their hotel. The sign hanging above the door proclaimed that it was called the Griffin.

There was a craggy man smoking outside as they approached.

'This pub any good?' Julian asked.

'Course it bloody is,' he said. 'It's my pub.'

'That's good enough for me,' said Julian. He was about to add, 'Come on, Dick, it's your round!' and charge inside. But he checked himself. 'What do you think?' he asked the others.

Dick and George raised their eyebrows at being consulted in such a respectful manner.

Seeing their hesitation, the landlord clinched the deal.

'It's quiz night,' he said.

The group gave a cheer.

'Woof!' said Timmy.

It wasn't just a good, cosy pub; it also served excellent food from the day's catch. They ate a dinner that left them in contented silence. Then they argued for a bit, pleasurably, and tried to engage the landlord in discussion, but he proved more impressively gruff with each exchange and they soon gave that up for a bad thing.

As the evening grew on, the pub started to fill up in preparation for the quiz. The landlord circulated and sheets were handed out.

'Team name?' Anne asked.

'Please, please, please,' Julian begged, 'don't suggest "Quiz Team Aguilera". That joke is older than time itself.'

George burped in his face.

'Just something nice,' Anne suggested. Then she heard herself. 'Oh, I don't care. Put what you like.'

'"The Secret Seven Suck"?' Dick suggested.

That cheered everyone up immensely, and was duly written on the top of the sheet.

'OKAY – IS EVERYONE READY?' boomed a voice cavernously from a speaker above their heads.

'You're already beautifully tanned,' she said.
'It seems such a waste.'
'It's for the best, believe me,' said Dick. 'I promise.'

Dick knocked his pint over and Julian nearly fell off his chair, trying to duck and throw his arms over his head simultaneously.

'Woof!' Timmy barked, shooting out of the pub door and setting off on a length of the beach.

'Sorry,' said the voice of the landlord. 'I had the volume turned up. Can you hear me now?'

'Yes!' chorused everyone in the pub.

'Right,' he said. 'Let's get going, then.'

Julian had often propounded to the group on the Ideal Pub Quiz. It was one that rewarded both specialist and general knowledge, and one that did not include questions on motorways, soap operas or (if possible) football. Each round of ten should include two severely difficult questions, two very easy ones, and six in between.

The perfect question – a very hard trick to pull off – was one that flattered the answerer. Meaning that they could get it right even though they did not know they knew the answer, but could discover it by a highly rewarding process of canny guesswork and deduction.

This quiz was a middling one. There were some questions about football, but this was leavened by the fact that there was a film round. There were a number from today's news, which made everyone feel foolish and frustrated for not having listened properly when the radio was on, and a picture round, which the team romped through with superlative ease.

There was a rather jolly team of local teachers on the next table, who were clearly practised quizzers and drinkers, and with whom the four (five, including Timmy) found themselves on good terms before much time had passed. Everyone in the pub seemed to grow more friendly and rowdy as the evening went on. At last, they came to the Jackpot Decider: a single question which had to be answered with complete precision, and on which rode the pub's cumulative jackpot. It seemed no one had got it right for several months, for the jackpot stood at well over two hundred pounds.

Dick whistled.

'Decent bunce,' said Julian. 'Come on, brains – let's do this.'

'The question is on literature,' said the landlord's voice, through the speaker.

Julian took a sharp breath.

'Nineteenth-century literature,' the landlord went on.

The teachers on the next table all threw up their hands, as though it was too much to bear, to have to answer questions about books outside of work. They engaged in a brief bout of good-humoured yodelling in order to let the landlord know what they thought of him.

'Specifically, the novels of Charles Dickens,' said the speaker.

'I fancy a shot of Sambuca,' said George, whom the others noted had been hitting it quite hard all evening. 'I'm on holiday, after all. Anyone else?'

'Shut up, shut up,' said Julian. Then he gripped her arm and begged her forgiveness. 'I might actually get this,' he said. He was trembling, and his pupils had dilated. He looked like he was having some sort of religious experience.

Which was not so very far from the truth. The novels of Charles Dickens were, to Julian, a thing of spiritual significance. He hadn't read them all, of course, because he was not yet thirty and there simply hadn't been the time. But he adored them, and his Oxford dissertation had been about them.

'In *Nicholas Nickleby*,' the landlord asked, 'the villain, Ralph Nickleby, commits suicide. How?'

That a quiz question – for a magnificent jackpot haul – could focus so narrowly on his favourite topic made Julian feel this moment had been created specially for him. The hour had cometh, he told himself in a somewhat garbled fashion, and so had the man.

'I know this,' he growled. 'He throws himself in the river. No!' He put his hand over his mouth and stared at the ceiling, afraid that his powers were failing him. He was still in this position when George got back from the bar with a round of Sambuca shots. Julian absentmindedly downed one as he wracked his brains. 'The house falls on him and crushes him to death!' he announced. 'That's it!'

'"The house falls on him",' repeated George as she wrote it on the answer sheet, '"and crushes him to—"'

'Wait!' said Julian. 'That might be from *Little Dorrit*. In *Nickleby*, he spontaneously combusts. No! That's in *Bleak House* . . .'

He was now riddled with self-doubt. George tapped the tip of her pen on the table rhythmically, waiting for him to reach a conclusion. Julian was going through all the methods of violent death in Dickens. Beheading: *A Tale of Two Cities*. Drowning: *David Copperfield*. Gunshot: *Bleak House* again. Clonked on the head and then drowned: *Our Mutual Friend*. But what about *Nickleby*?

'Come on, idiot,' said George.

'Poison,' Julian said. 'Bound to be. He poisons himself.'

They handed their sheet in and waited for the scores to be counted. Julian was pinched by nerves, going over it again and again in his head. He so badly wanted that jackpot . . .

None of them did a stroke of exercise,
or prepared in any way for the beach.

'OKAY!' boomed the voice a few minutes later, at a shattering volume. This created another mini-cyclone, with drinks knocked over and Timmy disappearing out on to the beach for another sprint.

'Sorry,' said the landlord, as he adjusted the mic's volume once again, after treating the whole pub to a sharpening whine. 'Okay. So, starting with the lowest scores first . . .' He read out a list of scores followed by team names – including, much to Julian's distaste, a 'Quiz Team Aguilera'.

'Now we're down to the final three. In third place, with thirty-eight points, it's The Teachers!'

The teachers on the next table booed heavily and stamped their feet.

'In second place, with a score of forty points, it's The Secret Seven Suck!'

'Ah, so close,' said Dick.

'DAMN IT,' said Julian.

'Heyyy!' shouted Anne and George in celebration.

'And, in first place . . . Wait, this is weird. Those team names are too similar . . .' There was a pause and a rustle while the landlord compared the papers in his hand. 'No, this seems to be right. In first place, with forty-one points, it's The Secret Seven!'

There was a loud cheer from a table on the other side

of the room, hidden by the crowd, accompanied by muted clapping.

'Those bastards,' said George.

'And what you're all waiting for: the Jackpot Decider. I can confirm someone got it right,' said the landlord.

'Poison, poison, poison, poison.'

'In *Nicholas Nickleby*, the character of Ralph commits suicide by hanging himself. Congratulations, Secret Seven, who take home the pot!'

There was another, even louder, cheer.

'I'm going to the bar,' said Julian, miserably.

'Sambuca!' shouted George after him.

'Such hard luck,' said a voice over Julian's shoulder as he stood at the bar. He turned to see Peter. 'Can I buy you a drink, Julian?'

'No, you c—' Julian began, then caught sight of the wad of notes in Peter's hand. 'Actually, a round of Sambucas wouldn't go amiss.'

'Delighted,' said Peter. 'And one for the dog? Or is he teetotal?'

Julian made the face of a gargoyle.

'Clever team name of yours,' said Peter. 'I must say, I was impressed.'

'Wot evs,' said Julian. 'Who got that *Nickleby* question, by the way?'

Peter indicated with a smile and inclination of his head that it was he.

'But you don't read books,' Julian said desperately. 'I know you don't. You're a bloody boring banker, or something. You've never read a book in your life.'

'Don't have to read the book,' Peter replied. 'Saw the film, didn't I? On a date with a particularly beautiful Brazilian lady, if memory serves . . .'

Julian chewed his knuckles with rage.

CHAPTER NINE

The First Day of Holiday

The next day, they rose later than intended, partly due to the Griffin's unexpectedly robust stock of Sambuca. Waking shortly before eleven, Dick decided it was his responsibility to open the curtains, and let the day in.

Sunshine blasted the room.

'Strewth!' said George.

'Oh my God, the world's on fire!' yelled Julian.

'My giddy aunt,' said Dick, rubbing his eyes.

'Let's go and get some breakfast,' Anne said, 'before my head falls off.'

Ducking out of the hotel as fast as possible in case they came face to face with their nemeses, the housemates found a little café down the street. They dismally perused the menu, ordered, ate, and soon afterwards found the holiday spirit returning.

'Let's leave exploring the countryside for tomorrow,' said Anne. 'I don't think I'm good for anything except a bout of sunbathing today.'

They all agreed, and repaired to the hotel to collect their things. Anne insisted that they all put on sunscreen and several other lotions. Then they snuck out (a habit which was quickly becoming tiresome) through the hotel lobby, to find a spot on the beach.

'Wait,' said George as they emerged on to the street. 'What the living heck are you wearing?'

'Who?' said Julian. 'Me? What's wrong with this?'

He looked down at his costume. His innocence made Dick and Anne laugh. It was a remarkably refreshing sensation. They weren't sure Julian had ever invited them to laugh at him before.

He was wearing an old pre-war bathing costume in white and blue stripes, that looked like a jaunty set of long johns. On his feet were tatty old flip-flops.

'Put a long twiddly moustache on you and shave your head, you could be an oldy-timey weightlifter,' said Dick.

'Not with that belly, he couldn't,' said Anne.

Julian was finding that holiday hangovers were wholly different from regular awful ones. In fact, being on holiday, he found that a ginormous truck-sized hangover, which would normally have knocked him flat for days on end, was rendered no worse than a background buzz. Although he had got a tad rowdy and bossy last night during the quiz, this morning he

was back to his new self, and once more enjoying the feeling
of having the weight of responsibility off his shoulders.

For instance, he didn't mind at all that the others were
making fun of him. In fact, he rather liked it. Instead of
responding, he donned his sunglasses and walked ahead of
them down the street with an exaggerated waddle, which
(combined with his bathing costume) made him look very
silly indeed.

'God,' George said. 'He's like an embarrassing dad.'

When they had found their spot on the beach and settled
down on their towels, Julian completed his costume with a
final flourish that produced guffaws from the others when
they saw it. Taking a large silk handkerchief, he tied knots
in the corners, and placed it on his head.

'Most Handsome Male,' said Dick.

'Ha!' screeched Anne, in a very unladylike manner.

'Oh, fuckballs,' said George.

They followed her gaze, which was fixed on a spot further
down the beach.

'Ugh,' said Julian.

Towards them came a group of seven immaculately handsome young people, bronzed and brilliant, running in perfect
formation. Peter was at the front, jogging backwards while

The woman on reception had pink bouffant hair and outrageously thick glasses through which she blinked enormously.

calling out the exercise regimen to the others. Gradually, his voice came within earshot.

'And . . . star-jump! And . . . squat-thrust! And . . . *wheel* those arms, one two three . . . And . . .'

'I thought they disbanded the Hitler Youth,' said Dick.

'And . . . say hello to the losers!' Peter called.

His six acolytes turned and waved merrily, giving a cheery chorus of, 'Hello, losers!', without breaking step.

In a moment, the Secret Seven had gone past. They disappeared all too slowly into the distance, oofing and gasping and stretching like their lives depended on it.

'I hope there's quicksand down there,' said Julian. 'Hey. Who wants an ice cream?'

'No one,' said Anne. 'I've just this minute finished my breakfast. Honestly, Julian. You'll have to buy the next-size-up bathing costume.'

'Ah,' said Dick. 'Body shaming, are we?'

Anne recoiled as if stung, looking aghast at this betrayal. Dick smiled.

'Not cool, Anne,' said George. She was, herself, attired in baggy white T-shirt, cargo shorts and dark glasses, and stretching back to enjoy the sun.

'Well,' Anne said. 'I'm sorry, Julian.'

'Oh, don't be stupid,' said Julian. 'You're my little sister;

you can say what you like. The important issue is, what are we going to do about this utter load-of-crap beach body contest?'

They all rested on their towels while they thought about it.

Dick started to snore gently, and then woke himself up by farting.

'Ahem,' he said. 'Excuse me.'

'You are, without doubt,' said Anne, fanning herself, 'the most . . .' Then she looked at Julian. 'The *second* most repulsive man in existence.'

'I think I've got an idea,' said George.

'You have?' Julian asked. 'In which case, before you tell us, may I make a suggestion? Ice-cream time! Last one to the ice-cream shop is a dirty body-shamer!' And, leaping up with reckless disregard for the possibility of pulling a muscle, or doing something to his back, Julian charged off into the distance, sand splaying off his flip-flops.

'Woof!' said Timmy, chasing after him.

'There really is something up with him,' said Anne. And then she thought to herself, Oh, shut up, Anne.

CHAPTER TEN

War and Pies

It was a Kirrin family rule that, when on holiday, everyone had to eat one ice cream every day. It had been imposed by a grandfather somewhere along the line to indulge children, and was strictly adhered to, even into adulthood.

Anne insisted on paying, and ordered that everyone have two scoops. She went for a scoop each of melon and raspberry sorbet, which drew admiring moans from the others. However, faced with a bank of tubs packed with rich flavours, her housemates found they could not resist the real, dairy kind.

George had a scoop of lemon cheesecake and one of cookie dough; Julian went for one of butterscotch-and-honeycomb and one salted Macadamia brittle; Dick said he'd like two scoops of vanilla . . .

'What are you saying?' Julian asked. 'VANILLA?'

'Wait for it,' Dick said, before turning back to the man behind the counter. 'And I'll avail myself of your coring service, please.' At which George, Anne and Julian looked up at the menu on the wall, sensing that they had missed a trick. Dick's two scoops of vanilla had a wide, deep cavity burrowed through each, into which were poured lavish gulps of two sauces: chocolate fudge and mint choc.

'Ooooooo . . .' said George.

'I admire your technique,' said Julian.

'Seems nice, if you like that sort of thing, I suppose,' said Anne.

They sat at a little cast-iron table on the street outside.

'Life's not that bad, is it,' said Julian, between licks. 'When you think about it.'

'Five million refugees homeless at this literal moment in time,' said George.

'Yes – good point. Sorry. Life's not bad, if you're white and upper middle class and privileged and us. Is it?'

'Steady on, guys,' said Dick. 'You're taking the shine off my holiday.'

Anne looked at him across the table. Dick had always been the one who looked after her. And, in gratitude for that, she had never really questioned him in any way. But now that she was starting to feel a little more independent, this favourite brother of hers was suddenly exposed to her scrutiny. She found his last remark disturbingly thoughtless and selfish. Glib, almost.

*The discovery of the Secret Seven in the same hotel
was a bitter blow to the group.*

She had never thought of him this way before, and it suddenly made her desperately unhappy; having perceived this one flaw, she worried it might be followed by a torrent of others she had always been blind to, which she couldn't bear. She decided to change the subject.

'So, George,' she said brightly. 'Tell us about this plan.'

'Hngh,' said George through a mouthful of ice cream. 'You'll love it. Did you see that shop down the street, which promises the best pies in Dorset?'

'See it? I've been smelling it since we got here,' said Julian.

'What's it called?' asked Dick. 'Mrs Crumpsnip, or something? Sounds like it's from a Dickens novel.'

'Don't mention Dickens, mate,' said Julian. 'Too soon.'

'Mrs Camblyton's Original Dorset Pies,' said George. 'That's the one.'

'Not sure I could fit a lunch in, though, so soon after this,' said Anne, taking another little lick of her ice cream. While the others had nearly finished wolfing their ices, Anne had made hardly any inroads into her sorbet, and was starting to regret asking for two scoops.

Timmy was by her chair, looking up, tongue lolling. Their eyes met, and they made a secret pact.

'Let's just finish these ice cream cones, and go over there,' said George. 'What do you think, Timmy?'

'Wulf!' said Timmy, through a mouthful of sorbet.

'So, let me get this straight,' said the stone-faced woman. 'Just run it by me again.'

George sighed. This was not going exactly as she had planned.

'Unless I'm mistaken,' the woman went on, before giving George a chance to run it by her again, 'you want to know how many pies I can make.'

'Yes,' George said.

'By tomorrow.'

'Well, yes.'

'For a pie-eating contest?'

'That's correct.'

'Because you object to the beach body contest we have here?'

'That's about the size of it, yes.'

'The one that's been running for over a hundred years?'

George left a dignified silence to allow the woman's heavy sarcasm to settle. 'That is the one I'm referring to,' she said. 'Yes.'

'Because of "body shaming",' the woman said flatly. 'Which is what exactly?'

Well, you ought to know, Anne thought, and then silently rebuked herself. God, she was noticing bad things in everyone today.

It turned out that the Mrs Crumpsnip (which was the name they now couldn't help associating with the place) depicted on the sign was not the current proprietress. The picture showed a wrinkly-faced grandmother in a pinny, all smiles and warm benevolence, handing over a tray of pies to a crowd of flat-capped workmen.

The current owner – possibly the original's granddaughter – was a rather pitiless individual of indeterminate age, who seemed to take no pleasure in anything other than slowing down conversations, forcing people to repeat themselves, and maintaining a rigid and stone-like expression. Around the back of the shop prowled a mean-faced ginger tabby, his tail flicking dismissively.

George found this woman rather wonderful, in an objective sense, but with regard to her current purpose, she was proving to be something of an obstacle. Forcing George to repeat each and every question, and then requesting her to sum up afterwards, as she did, made it sound as though George had asked her to assemble the Hoover Dam, from matchsticks, in three-quarters of an hour.

But this was a pie shop, George kept reminding herself, so she refused to be made to feel stupid for coming in and asking for pies. She persisted.

'So, can you do it?' George asked.

'Can I do it?' the woman asked.

'Ugh,' George said, turning her head away and rubbing an eye with the ball of her thumb. 'My hangover's coming back.'

'I feel your pain, man,' Julian muttered into her ear. 'I'd have lamped her long ago.'

'Yes,' the woman said.

'Yes?' George asked.

'Now they're both at it,' said Anne.

'Of course I can,' said Ms Camblyton. 'It's a pie shop, innit?'

'Well, I don't know,' said George. 'I thought there might be some sort of limit on your daily output.'

'There is that,' she said. 'But, look here,' she elegantly thumped a nearby door with one of her buttocks and pointed into the storeroom, which boasted a walk-in freezer. 'Got two thousand pies in there, haven't I? Best pies in Dorset,' she added.

*The novels of Charles Dickens were, to Julian,
a thing of spiritual significance.*

'Great. Fine. That's good,' said George. 'How much would that cost? To buy them all?'

'How much would it cost?' the woman asked.

'Yes.'

'For all two thousand?'

'Please, sweet baby Jesus on a motorbike, give me strength,' whispered George. 'Yes. How much?'

'I'll do you a special offer,' said the woman. 'Four and a half grand.'

'What I don't entirely understand,' said Dick, as they walked away down the street, 'is how much you thought they were going to cost?'

'It's a fair point,' said George. 'I suppose the sign made me think she would be a lovely, kind old lady, and that she'd understand my point about standing up to this body-image crap – although, I see now, those two won't necessarily go together – and I guessed she'd give me a proper discount, or allow me to pay it in stages, or something.'

'So our protest, which was to hold a pie-eating contest right next to or in front of the Best Beach Body Competition, or whatever it's called,' said Dick, 'is dead in the water?'

'Yes. Unlike the Secret Seven, unfortunately,' said George. 'We'll have to think of something else to scupper their plans.'

'Hey, Timmy?' Julian suddenly said. 'What's that I see?'

'Woof?' asked Timmy.

'The sea, mate! Race you there!'

He set off, galumphing along the street in his flip-flops, as Timmy shot past him with a 'woof!'.

CHAPTER ELEVEN

Revels and Repercussions

They all went into the sea eventually. Julian and Timmy splashed about, while the others went for a proper swim, feeling cooled and joyful and liberated from gravity, and generally on holiday.

They came back to the hotel to shower and change, and then, feeling happy and careless, they went down into the hotel bar. If the Secret Seven fancied popping up in here, they could go right ahead and see what happened.

What *did* in fact happen was that events quickly snowballed. Firstly, the SS failed to show ('The abbreviation tells you everything,' said George), which cheered them up enormously; secondly, a live skiffle band set up in the corner of the bar and started to play, which was so unexpected it generated a sort of low-level hilarity; thirdly, the team of teachers from the previous night's quiz turned up and, spotting their old rivals, they cheered, and joined them at their table.

It quickly emerged that teachers could *drink*. Julian realized he was drunk around midnight, when he tried, for the fourteenth time in a row, to get their names right.

'And your name's Phil?' he asked.

'Phil Hadgett,' said Phil Hadgett. 'That's Dan Light, this is Dave Sadler.'

'Phil Sallett,' Julian nodded. 'Goddit. Davc!' he shouted at Dan. 'You goin' t'other ba'?'

'I was, yeah,' Dan said. 'Are you sure you need another drink?'

'I'm sure as you like!' Julian intended to shout. What he actually said was a cluster of syllables that roughly conveyed his meaning, without belonging to any recorded language.

Mysteriously, Anne, George and Dick seemed to be faring better that Julian. They were dancing. Perceiving this fact, Julian realized that he had never seen Dick dance. He tried to focus, but his eyes wouldn't do it.

'Woah, there,' Dave Sadler said good humouredly, gently nudging Julian back on to his stool at the exact moment he was about to fall off it. Looking somewhat dubious, he handed over the pint of cider that Dan had brought back from the bar.

'You teachers can drink, you know that?' Julian asked.

'Comes with the territory,' Dave said. 'Are you sure you're all right?'

Julian was finding that holiday hangovers were wholly different from regular awful ones.

'Yeah,' said Julian. 'It's on holiday. Yeah!' And he thrust his drink up in the air with a victorious punch, displacing half of it on to his own head.

'Why do holidays have to be like this?' said a voice. 'I'm going to have to go back to work, just to feel well again!'

Julian tried to turn over, and found that he couldn't. He briefly wondered whether he was in hospital, and decided to try to sleep for another half hour to see if the various things making him miserable might have sorted themselves out by then.

'Oh, jeez,' croaked a voice somewhere nearby. It gave a cough, and then another cough. It followed this with a much longer and louder succession of coughs, followed by a gargling rasp of phlegm and a glutinous expectoration. 'Oh, jeez,' it said again.

Fuck it, thought Julian. I'm going to have to get up.

Opening his eyes and seeing nothing, he refused to panic. Finding himself unable to move his legs, he once more refused to panic. Gradually, he worked out that, in his sleep, he had wrapped himself in a sheet. Having established this fact, by a sequence of tiny manoeuvres, he then succeeded in spinning himself round and loosening the sheet enough to get a hand out. From there, it was plain sailing, and soon he was able to move freely and was taking deep, replenishing breaths. The whole process had taken about half an hour.

There were further challenges in store, though.

First, he was in total darkness. By sitting up and bashing his head on the underside of a sink, Julian deduced he was in a bathroom. He fervently hoped it was *his* bathroom.

He then carefully got to his feet, and tottered to the nearest wall. He felt along it until he found a light switch. The resultant searing blast of light made him yell fearfully, and he hammered at the light switch with his fist until it went off again.

He leant against the wall, panting, as the pain receded. In the brief moment of light, he had spotted the location of the door, and so presently he threw this open. He was relieved to see the vaguely familiar contours of a hotel room and three sleeping lumps that roughly corresponded to his travelling companions.

Timmy licked his hand, which was a deeply reassuring sensation.

'Think I'll go out and get some fresh air,' Julian said.

None of the shapes moved.

'Bet you're hungover,' said Julian. 'You lot should be ashamed of yourselves.'

A pillow hurtled towards him out of the darkness. He

ducked under it, and slipped out of the door, with Timmy in tow.

Julian walked along the streets around the hotel as gently as possible, trying to piece together the events of the previous evening.

He vaguely remembered an establishment called the Blue Cow, and a cider festival. And some sort of ruckus or other . . . but he didn't think he had been involved. And there was a drink called 'Old Rosie', which had made him feel – all too briefly – like Superman.

'Oh, golly, Timmo,' said Julian. 'It just doesn't bear thinking about.'

'Woof,' Timmy agreed.

They came on to the beach, but, aside from the preparations for the beach body contest, there was very little action to see this early in the morning. Which was how early, exactly? Julian checked his phone, but found that it had died.

They walked along the sand, and Julian threw a few sticks, until they came to the frontage of La Credenza. As part of its renovations, the whole place was being repainted – and by an interesting method. Rather than a bunch of chaps on scaffolding, with rollers and brushes, the roof and windows had been covered off with sheeting and masking tape, and it was being sprayed by a vigorous-looking young man with a nozzle that led back to a large tank of paint on a flatbed truck. The painting was just beginning, and Julian examined the shade.

'Bright green,' he reflected. 'How charming.' He turned back, deciding that he was working up an appetite for breakfast, and he was feeling nearly well enough to go back to the room and taunt the others afresh.

As he walked, Julian drank in the sunshine. God, it was good. He didn't believe you could get better sunshine than this in Italy, or California, or anywhere. He closed his eyes and turned his face towards it for as long as he dared, and was startled out of his pleasant bask by a loud beep close behind.

'Get off the road, you filthy maniac!' roared a voice.

Julian leapt out of the way, then turned to look. It was the same old man they had seen driving down the beach on their first day – a man who, up close, Julian could see was eighty if he was a day – driving a 1920s jalopy and wearing driving goggles. He was going at about six miles an hour. The man glared at Julian and squeezed the horn again – which it seemed had developed some sort of rip, because this time it just let out a wheeze followed by a whine.

Now, that's more like the Dorset I know, thought Julian, as

It was a Kirrin family rule that, when on holiday,
everyone had to eat one ice cream every day.

he watched the car drive off, incredibly slowly, meandering all over the road.

Thinking of the Dorset he knew, Julian had an idea. He popped along to the pie shop, to conduct some brief business, and was relieved to find it open. He then made his way back to the hotel and up to the room. He didn't have the key, so he knocked tentatively.

He heard three distinct groans from within the room; Timmy responded with a bark. Eventually, the door cracked open, and Dick retreated into the darkness, to his bed.

'Leave me alone,' Dick said. 'I never want to talk to anyone again.'

'Balls,' said Julian. 'Get up and smell the coffee.'

'You brought coffee?' George asked from beneath her one remaining pillow.

'Well, no. I was speaking figuratively.'

And so saying, he flung open the curtains. There was a cacophony of protests, and some further barking. He told himself that he was Acting For Their Own Good, rather than taking charge.

Then, turning round, he saw why – hangovers aside – they had all been so hungry for shadow.

'What the *bloody hell* has happened here?' he asked. 'Anne! My God!'

The room itself was intact. It was the people who were showing signs of wear.

'Oh, shush,' said Anne, sitting up in bed. She had an absolute peach of a black eye. It was still developing, and looked likely to get bigger and blacker yet. You could see already it was the kind that would fade slowly, in gorgeous delicate shades, like a sunset.

'It's nothing,' she said. 'And don't get all boring and macho and try to defend my honour; I can't imagine anything more tedious. It was a simple misunderstanding.'

Julian was, of course, in the process of getting all boring and macho and intending to defend her honour. He couldn't help it – she was his little sister. The adrenalin was already pumping.

'So someone punched you?'

'A bit,' Anne said. 'But it was me who was defending the honour.'

'Of who?' Julian asked. 'Of whom?' he corrected himself. Then he was unsure again; he'd read somewhere – in Kingsley Amis's *The King's English*, he thought – that 'whom' was now outdated and redundant. He so hated to be linguistically inaccurate. Then he realized that he was allowing himself to get distracted. '*Whose*?' he asked, at last.

'Mine,' said Dick. 'She was standing up for me.'

Julian gaped at him. Dick blinked back, unamused. Right down the centre of his luscious head of dark hair was carved a wide strip of shaved scalp.

'You remember that family we met at the cider festival?' Anne asked. 'We'd all had a few too many, and went back to their house. The girl was called Ruby, and it seemed to me she had taken a shine to Dick. But apparently her brothers just wanted to play a trick on him. Next thing we knew, he had this new hairstyle.'

'But that doesn't explain how you got the black eye,' Julian said.

Anne shrugged. 'She had it coming.'

'So you *plugged* her one, Anne?'

'Right in the jaw,' Dick said. 'I've never seen anything so cool in my life. It was worth getting this for.' He ran his hand through his hair, but grimaced as he felt the stubbly scalp against his palm.

'My hand doesn't feel right,' said Anne. 'Is there such a thing as a dislocated knuckle?'

'*Good girl!*' said Julian. He'd never felt such a burst of pride.

Anne wasn't impressed. 'I don't really mind whether you think I'm a good girl or a bad girl, to be honest.'

'Oh, yes. Sorry,' Julian said.

He turned finally to George. She awaited his comments with dull-eyed boredom.

'So, George,' he said. 'That's an interesting decision.'

'After three pints of Rosie on top of everything else, I'm not sure it's fair to call it a decision.'

'Fair dos,' said Julian. 'But, bloody hell, how did you manage to find a tattoo artist, at two a.m., in a tiny place like this?'

'He's an amateur, isn't he?' she answered.

'Pretty good for an amateur,' Julian said, looking closer. 'I mean, the lines are clean. Not sure I'd have gone with a phrase in Japanese script, myself. What does it mean?'

'I think it means I'm a dickhead,' said George. 'Pretty picture we'll make for the beach body contest, isn't it, Timmy?'

'Woof,' Timmy answered guardedly, not wanting to be tricked into insulting his friends.

'I think I've had about enough of this place,' said George. 'How about we get out of here before the beach body fiasco, catch some breakfast on the station and go on home? There's a new David Attenborough thing starting tonight – about molluscs or toads or something.'

'Ooooo,' said Anne and Dick.

'So it features the Secret Seven, then?' Julian asked.

'Woof!' said Timmy.

CHAPTER TWELVE

The Best Hangover Cure Ever

Moving like lightning, they all decided to close the curtains and doze for another hour or two. Then they rose again, feeling a little better rested but far more groggy, and packed.

As they went to leave, the four of them were keen to attract as little attention as possible. But there was no inching their way out of the foyer this time, as the bill had to be paid. Dick (who was once more wearing a bandana – improvised by Anne from a spare T-shirt) did this with quick dispatch, and then they stepped as discreetly as possible into the street.

'Oh, *rats*,' said Julian. 'Bloody road takes us past where they're holding the stupid beauty pageant.'

'Slow and steady,' said Anne.

'Calm and collected,' said Dick. 'We'll sneak past.'

They crept along the seafront as inconspicuously as four people can when accompanied by suitcases and a dog – and sporting a black eye, a new tattoo, and a reverse Mohican.

They had got fifty yards and, in defiance of their hangovers,

'So, our protest, which was to hold a pie-eating
contest, is dead in the water?'
'Yes. Unlike the Secret Seven, unfortunately.' said George.'

were starting to feel optimistic about their chances, when a huge voice echoed out at them.

'DO WE HAVE SOME LATE ENTRANTS TO THE COMPETITION?' it asked.

They all froze.

'What is it with Dorset and amplifiers?' asked George, her hands over her ears.

They turned to look at the beach. They were faced with exactly the spectacle they had been trying to avoid. There was a podium, with three levels for first, second and third place. They saw at once that the voice on the tannoy was not seriously inviting them to take part, but trying to attract attention and swell the somewhat thin crowd of spectators. It appeared the contest was already over – all three places on the podium were already filled by members of the Secret Seven.

Anne, Dick and George stepped forward to get a closer look at the winners. On the top spot was Peter, as he (and no doubt everyone else in shouting distance) had expected. He was brandishing the Most Handsome Male sash. Barbara – next to him, in second place – was visibly delighted by the sight of Anne's black eye, and smiled complacently as she twirled the Most Beautiful Female sash over her shoulder and around her waist. In third place was Colin—

'TOOT, TOOT!' yelled a voice, accompanied by the sound of a gear-grinding, petrol-guzzling motor. 'Are you blind, as well as deaf, as well as STUPID?'

'Oh, shit,' said George, grabbing Timmy and jumping for both of their lives.

Julian, recognizing the voice, remained calm. He had seen the car's average velocity and suspected that, if it hit him, with the extra weight he was carrying after his beach body preparations, it might very well be the car that came off worse. Instead of jumping, he turned slowly.

It had clearly never occurred to the driver that this might happen – he seemed entirely unprepared for the eventuality. He panicked.

The car veered this way and then that, as wildly as something can, that is going only slightly faster than ambling pace. It missed Julian, and came to rest with a loud crunch, against the back of the truck that held the tank of paint. Then it was the giant paint canister's turn to wobble, and then totter, and finally roll from its perch on to the ground with a loud, deep, metallic clang.

Everyone – the old man, Anne and Dick, Peter and Barbara, the announcer with his microphone, everyone on the beach – froze.

Then Anne and Dick recovered their wits sufficiently to

leap forward and drag the man from his car. They pulled him to safety behind the vehicle, where they were joined by Julian, George and Timmy, just at the moment that the paint container sprung a leak.

From behind the car, they heard an intense fizzing sound, which escalated to a gushing noise, lasting for about thirty seconds. Then there came a much lighter metallic ringing sound as, its energy and contents spent, the tank came to rest. This was hardly audible, though, above the screaming.

Dick, Julian, Anne, George and the driver (who removed his goggles to get a better look) all trotted towards the beach, trying to make sense of what they saw.

The observers of the beach body competition had just about scrambled to safety, and were scattered in the distance. The victors were, however, not so lucky. The podium and all three winners had been utterly covered, from head to toe, in bright green paint. They were looking down at themselves as the excess of paint fell in droplets from their hair and dribbled down the perfectly sculpted lines of their bodies.

It was Peter, standing tallest and foremost among them, who had taken the brunt of it. And so, when he rose to speak, he made a completely unrecognizable figure.

'You—' he said, then he slipped on some paint and went

over. He landed on the beach with a thump and, when he stood up again, was covered along the length of his body by a grimy matrix of paint and sand.

'Oh, PETER!' yelled Barbara. And, in her desperation to reach him and help, she slipped too, performing something along the lines of a three-quarters cartwheel in mid-air (which drew applause from the scattered audience) and landing face-first on the beach.

When they had helped each other to their feet, Barbara and Peter gazed at one another, saw what they looked like, and screamed. They both ran off into the distance, presumably to escape the scrutiny of the crowd and to throw themselves into the ocean for as long as it took to get the mess off.

'Best hangover cure ever,' said Dick.

It took a little while for the hilarity on the beach to die down. When it was starting to, however, the four housemates (and a rather overexcited Timmy) found themselves standing near a beachfront pub table on which had been arranged a huge selection of delicious-looking pies.

'What's this?' asked George.

'Well, we don't need to eat two thousand of them,' said Julian. 'But I thought, seeing as we've slept in until nearly lunchtime and had no breakfast, a small, informal pie-eating contest might be arranged. So I popped in this morning and

'Why do holidays have to be like this?'
said a voice. 'I'm going to have to go back to work,
just to feel well again!'

ordered a couple of dozen. Here,' he said to the elderly driver, 'I'm sorry about your car. Have a pie to settle the nerves?'

'Don't bloody mind if I bloody do,' said the old gent. 'Sorry for yelling at you, and all that.'

'Please,' said Anne. 'Don't think of it. You've given us the best present we could ever have.'

'Second best hangover cure ever,' said Dick, through a mouthful of pie. He looked along the table at the extraordinary selection. He was already halfway through a ham and leek pie, and was eyeing up a beef and oyster one to try next . . .

'Do you mind if we join you?' asked a voice.

With utter astonishment, the four friends found themselves looking up at Janet and the remaining three of the Secret Seven, whose names none of them could ever remember.

'It's just, we never really wanted to join in with this beach body stuff,' Janet said. 'We were forced to by beastly Peter. He can be such a pill sometimes. I say, we're so terribly grateful to you for shaming him like that. Maybe he won't be such a bully in future,' she said, albeit without much confidence.

'Sit down,' said Dick. 'Join us!'

'Please,' said Anne.

The three guests did so, with evident pleasure. They did

their level best to offer convincing compliments on Dick's bandana and George's tattoo, and showed genuine concern over Anne's black eye.

'You should see the other girl,' Anne said.

'This is *so* nice,' said Janet. 'I'm delighted to show that there's no real animosity between us. From us four, anyway. And, after all these months of enforced dieting, we *are* jolly hungry . . .'

'Get stuck in, by all means!' said Julian. Seeing how Peter made his companions feel made Julian even gladder to have shed his mantle of Boy Who Always Takes Charge. Long may it continue, he thought. He was also delighted to see everyone tucking into pies with the dogged determination of people who had not the slightest regard for their beach bodies.

'Best Dorset holiday ever, I reckon. Eh, Timmy?'

'Woof!' yelled Timmy. 'Woof, woof!'